A great start to KS2 Grammar from CGP!

This Foundation SAT Buster is perfect for pupils who find KS2 English tough going. It's packed with friendly practice to build up the basic Grammar skills they'll need for the SATs in Year 6.

We've included plenty of helpful hints and tips along the way, plus model answers to show them what they're aiming for.

There are also fun self-assessment boxes for each topic, plus a scoresheet to keep track of their overall marks. We've thought of everything!

What CGP is all about

Our sole aim here at CGP is to produce the highest quality books — carefully written, immaculately presented and dangerously close to being funny.

Then we work our socks off to get them out to you — at the cheapest possible prices.

Published by CGP

Editors: Andy Cashmore, Catherine Heygate, Hannah Roscoe

ISBN: 978 1 78908 428 3

With thanks to Amanda MacNaughton and Glenn Rogers for the proofreading.
Also thanks to Emily Smith for the copyright research.

Printed by Elanders Ltd, Newcastle upon Tyne.
Clipart from Corel®

Based on the classic CGP style created by Richard Parsons.

Contents

Here's what you have to do...

In Year 6 you have to take some tests called the SATs.
This book will help you do well in the grammar bit of the tests.

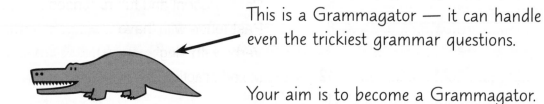

This is a Grammagator — it can handle even the trickiest grammar questions.

Your aim is to become a Grammagator.

Work through the questions in the book. When you finish a topic, add up your marks and write them in the scoresheet at the end of the book.

Then, put a tick in the box at the end of the topic to show how you got on.

If you got a lot of grammar questions wrong, put a tick in the circle on the left. Don't worry — every Grammagator has to start somewhere. Go over your grammar rules again, then have another go.

If you're nearly there but still got some grammar questions wrong, put a tick in the middle circle. Ask your teacher to help you work out the areas you need more practice on.

If you felt really confident and got nearly all the questions right, tick the circle on the right.

Congratulations — you're a Grammagator!

Grammar Hints and Tips

Grammar can be a bit tricky, so get a firm grip on the basics and you'll be off to a good start. Here are some hints and tips for the most important bits of grammar.

1. **Learn** the **main parts** of speech.

    The <u>horse</u> <u>trotted</u> along the <u>muddy</u> road.

    Noun   **Verb**   **Adjective**
    (a naming word)   (a doing or   (a describing word)
                 being word)

2. Make sure you can **identify** the different **parts** of a **sentence**.

    <u>When it rains,</u> <u>the horse loves playing in the mud.</u>

    Subordinate Clause   **Main Clause**
    (a less important clause) (the most important clause —
                   it makes sense on its own)

3. Make sure that the **verb agrees** with whoever is doing the action.

    The <u>horse jumps</u> in the puddle.   The <u>horses jump</u> in the puddle.

    There is **only one** horse, so   There's **more than one** horse,
    the verb needs to be **singular**.   so the verb needs to be **plural**.

4. Check that **verbs** are written correctly in each **tense**.

    He <u>has worn</u> a coat.   He <u>wore</u> a coat.

    Not He <u>has wore</u> a coat.   **Not** He <u>worn</u> a coat.

5. Know how to spot **Non-Standard English**, like double negatives.

    He has <u>not</u> worn <u>no</u> coat.   He has not worn a coat.

    This is a **double negative**.   This is **Standard English**.

Nouns

Warm Up

Nouns are words that name things — the names of places, people and your favourite dessert are all nouns. Try this warm up question to check you know what a noun is...

1) Circle the words below that are nouns.

| plane | huge | garage | snake |
| collide | Emily | lazy | depart |

Now try these questions to practise using nouns.

2) Rewrite each sentence, replacing the words in bold with different nouns.

Riyad hates going to the **dentist**.

Mum hates going to the **cinema**.

The **dolphin** I saw in **Spain** was beautiful.

....

Pizza is my favourite **food**.

....

2 marks

3) Choose an appropriate noun to go in the space in each of these sentences.

Tommy built a brand new ....

The dogs loved to chase ....

The .... was incredibly smelly.

2 marks

Grammagators know a noun when they see one. Do you? Tick a box to show how you got on.

Singular and plural nouns

Warm Up

A singular noun tells you that there is one of something. A plural noun means there is more than one. Make sure you know the difference by answering this question...

1) In the boxes below, write whether each noun is singular (S) or plural (P).

tomatoes ☐   house ☐   cake ☐   coats ☐

tree ☐   parents ☐   event ☐   players ☐

A plural noun normally ends in 's' or 'es'.

Have a go at these questions all about singular and plural nouns.

2) For each pair of words in brackets, circle the correct form of the noun.

The squirrel hid all of its (**acorn** / **acorns**) at the bottom of the garden.

The brave (**woman** / **women**) was dancing with a snake.

The (**ferry** / **ferries**) was about to leave without me.

My (**shoe** / **shoes**) are too large for my feet.

2 marks

3) Complete the table below with the nouns in their singular and plural form.

Singular	Plural
....	pockets
bus	....
tooth	....
....	berries

Some plural nouns don't end in 's' or 'es'.

2 marks

Grammagators don't get singular and plural nouns mixed up. How did you do? Tick the box.

Types of noun

There are different types of noun. Give this question a go to see if you can spot them...

1) Complete the table by circling the example that fits each definition.

Type of noun	Definition	Example
Common noun	General words for things, animals and people.	(parrot)/ Italy
Proper noun	Names of particular people, places or things — they always start with a capital letter.	**Richard / lawn**
Collective noun	Words for groups of animals or people.	**person / crowd**
Abstract noun	Words for things you cannot see, hear, smell, taste or touch, like ideas and emotions.	**joy / butter**

Next are some questions on these different types of noun for you to try.

2) Join each noun (in a white box) with the type of noun it is (in a grey box).
   Use the definitions from the warm up question to help you.

January		hope	
Common noun	boats	herd	Collective noun
Proper noun	spinach	Julia	Abstract noun
	gang	relief	

2 marks

3) Tick the **two** sentences that use common nouns.

The soup she ate at the restaurant was spicy. ☐

Dev lived in India before moving to England. ☐

My cat is scared of other animals. ☐

2 marks

Types of noun

4) Underline all the proper nouns in the sentences below.

Jamal said his trip to Egypt last year was amazing.

Use the definition of a proper noun in the warm up to help you.

On Tuesday we are going to visit Chrissie at her friend's house.

We sailed across the Atlantic Ocean to get to America.

_____
2 marks

5) Tick the words below which are abstract nouns.

Remember, abstract noun are things you cannot see, hear, smell, taste or touch.

hate ☐   tyre ☐   leaf ☐   courage ☐

trust ☐   cactus ☐   event ☐   excitement ☐

_____
2 marks

6) Fill in the blanks with collective nouns from the box below.

~~swarm~~   flock   school   pack

The ....swarm........ of bees chased the .... of wolves.

The .... of ducks flew over the .... of fish.

_____
2 marks

7) Read the sentence below. Write each noun in bold next to the type of noun it is.

Bella was filled with **delight** when she saw the **fleet** of ships in the **harbour**.

Common noun — ....   Proper noun — ....

Collective noun — ....   Abstract noun — ....

_____
2 marks

Grammagators are experts at identifying different types of noun. Tick a box to show how you did.

Section 1 — Types of Word

Pronouns

Warm Up

Pronouns can be used instead of nouns. You can use them to help your sentences flow.

1) Tick the words below which are pronouns.

date ☐	**us** ☐	**Giles** ☐	**he** ☐
her ☐	**person** ☐	**twins** ☐	**you** ☐

Now you're warmed up, see how well you know pronouns with these questions.

2) Match each noun to the most appropriate pronoun.

Craig	Laura	swans

they	him	she

2 marks

3) Write down who or what the pronoun in bold refers to in each sentence below.

Cakes were brought in for the class. **They** were eaten within minutes.

....

Bruno asked Sarah for a lift because **he** was running late for judo.

....

2 marks

4) Replace the underlined phrases with the correct pronoun.

My friend and I tried the game and <u>my friend and I</u> liked it.

⬆

Ben was good at hitting the ball, but <u>Ben</u> didn't pass <u>the ball</u> very much.

⬆ ⬆

2 marks

Pronouns

5) Fill in the blanks with pronouns from the box below.

| she | we | it | ~~they~~ |

The eagles looked incredibly large when ....they........ got nearer.

Jabir and I peered into the river, but .... couldn't see any fish.

Paula drew a picture, then .... threw .... away. _____
2 marks

6) For each pair of words in brackets, circle the correct pronoun.

Simon's teacher said (**he** / **him**) should read more books.

Mum told (**I** / **me**) to eat the food (**I** / **me**) had on my plate.

(**They** / **Them**) were fast, but not fast enough to catch (**us** / **we**). _____
2 marks

7) Circle the words below that are possessive pronouns.

Possessive pronouns show who things belong to.

| (his) | she | us |
| me | mine | hers |

_____
2 marks

8) Fill in the blanks with the possessive pronouns you circled above.

He decided who played on the slide because it was ....his........ .

I lost my unicorn, so Yasmine let me borrow ....

The treasure was .... because I found it. _____
2 marks

Tricky pronouns don't trip up the best Grammagators.
Tick the box to show how you found them.

Section 1 — Types of Word

Determiners

Warm Up

A determiner is a little word like 'a', 'the' or 'some' that goes before a noun or noun phrase.
The words 'a', 'an' and 'the' are the most common determiners, but there are lots more...

1) Choose **a** or **an** to go in front of each of the words below.

............a............ brick .... flame .... ostrich

.... insect .... artist .... crane

Next up are some more questions to help you practise using determiners.

2) Circle the correct determiner in the sentences below.

Shanice found (**a** / **the**) envelope for her brother.

I only have (**a** / **an**) little bit of milk on my cereal.

Are you frightened of (**an** / **the**) troll that lives under the bridge?

> Try saying the sentence out loud to see which determiner sounds like it makes the most sense.

2 marks

3) Draw lines to match each sentence with the correct missing determiner.

I can't solve .... clue.		many
.... creatures live deep underwater.		this
There isn't .... ice-cream left.		much

2 marks

4) Underline the **four** determiners in the sentence below.

Ellie asked the man for a pen so she could get an autograph from the actor.

2 marks

Grammagators love chomping down on determiners.
Tick a box to show if you feel happy with them.

Verbs

Warm Up

Verbs are action words — they show what a person or thing is doing or being.
Have a go at this warm up question to see if you can spot verbs...

1) Circle the words below that are verbs.

| chilly | wrote | meal | carrot |

| did | loyal | speak | create |

Answering questions about verbs is the best way to get used to them — away you go.

2) Put a tick in the boxes that point to a verb.

I visit my Grandma once a month and we play board games.

There are two verbs in each sentence.

Sandra brought me a blanket and I slept on the comfy sofa.

_____
2 marks

3) Circle the **two** verbs in each sentence.

The thief sneaked into the museum and stole the jewel.

The artist paints a picture and gives it to her friend.

_____
2 marks

4) The verb in each sentence below has been used incorrectly. Underline the incorrect verb and write the correct form on the dotted line.

Daniel <u>buy</u> a magazine for his sister.   buys
....

The sentences should all be in the present tense.

The woman run away from the angry chicken.
....

We gives money to charity each year.
....

_____
2 marks

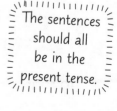

Verbs

5) Draw lines to match each sentence to the
   name of the person who is doing the action.

   | Clara passes the ketchup to Joe. |

   | In Clara's bag, Joe found his book. |

   Clara

   | Joe trips over Clara's leg. |

   Joe

   | Clara tossed Joe's ball to him. |

   _____
   2 marks

6) Circle the correct form of the verb for each sentence.

   Marie and I (**jumps** / **jump**) on the bed to wake my brother up.

   My teacher (**reward** / **rewards**) students for good behaviour.

   The police officers (**chase** / **chases**) the criminal down the street.

   _____
   2 marks

7) Complete each sentence using the present tense form of the verb in brackets.

   The seal ......*dives*...... (**to dive**) into the water.

   Harry .... (**to go**) to the bank.

   We .... (**to dance**) to our favourite songs.

   _____
   2 marks

8) Write a sentence using the verbs and the animals given below.

   to search   the pandas

   You can use the past or the present tense.

   ....

   to roar   the lion

   ....

   _____
   2 marks

Verbs

9) Tick the words below which are modal verbs.

can ☐   **said** ☐   **shall** ☐

ask ☐   **agreed** ☐   **might** ☐

try ☐   **would** ☐   **must** ☐

Modal verbs are words like 'may' and 'should'. They can show how likely something is.

2 marks

10) Underline the modal verb in each sentence.

The restaurant will open at five o'clock.

Tamara could go to the hairdresser on Saturday.

The spaceship may land on a new planet tomorrow.

2 marks

11) Tick the **two** sentences where the modal verb shows certainty.

Our neighbour will water our garden while we are away. ☐

I shall wear my seat belt when I'm in the car. ☐

My brother's magic tricks can be quite good. ☐

Certainty means that something is definitely going to happen.

2 marks

12) Rewrite these sentences using the correct modal verb from the brackets.

I (**may / might / will**) definitely come camping with you.

....

Anna (**shall / will / may**) defeat the wrestler, but it's not certain.

....

2 marks

Verbs are as fun as an afternoon swim for a Grammagator. How did you get on with them?

Section 1 — Types of Word

Adjectives

Adjectives are words that describe nouns. They can tell you how something looks or feels. They can also tell you how something makes you feel, e.g. a <u>happy</u> story...

1) Tick the words below which are adjectives.

short ☐	**slowly** ☐	**amusing** ☐	**steamy** ☐
rocky ☐	**thunder** ☐	**hiking** ☐	**clouds** ☐

Now it's time to practise using adjectives by answering these questions.

2) Put a tick in the boxes that point to an adjective.

The brown horse trotted slowly because his legs were tired.

☐ ☐ ☐ ☐

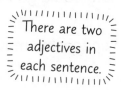
There are two adjectives in each sentence.

The jolly gnome skipped through the green grass.

☐ ☐ ☐ ☐

Briony was exhausted after skiing down the snowy hill.

☐ ☐ ☐ ☐

_____
2 marks

3) Underline the adjectives in the sentences below.

The goat was <u>surprised</u>.

Ling had a red scarf on.

Adam didn't win because he was unlucky.

The noisy crowd cheered the talented singer.  *These sentences have more than one adjective.*

The sluggish bus was overtaken by the speedy taxi.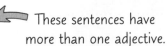

_____
2 marks

Adjectives

4) Join each noun below with the most appropriate adjective.

library	party	carpet	hill

silent	shaggy	steep	enjoyable

2 marks

5) Circle the adjective that fits each sentence best.

The (**tired** / **lively**) child slept on the journey home.

The lake is full of rubbish, so its water is (**murky** / **clear**).

The snow is (**freezing** / **scorching**) and (**crunchy** / **cosy**).

2 marks

6) Fill in the blanks with adjectives from the box below.

> tiniest   starving   delicious   delighted

My stomach was rumbling because I was .... When

Dad finally served dinner, I was .... However, my portion

of .... curry was the .... I have ever seen.

2 marks

7) Rewrite the sentence below, replacing the underlined adjectives
    with more interesting ones. Use a different word each time.

The <u>big</u> elephant crossed the <u>big</u> river and ate <u>big</u> leaves from the <u>big</u> tree.

The gigantic elephant ....

....

2 marks

*Grammagators can be described as ace when it comes
to adjectives. How amazing do you feel about them?*

Section 1 — Types of Word

Adverbs

Warm Up

Adverbs describe verbs, adjectives and other adverbs. Here's a warm up to get started...

1) Circle all the adverbs in the box below.

> lily   sadly   jumpy   silently
> warily   sleepy   tidily

Build your adverb knowledge by moving swiftly on to these questions.

2) Tick the **two** sentences that use adverbs.

The pigeons ate the bread greedily. ☐

The mermaid's favourite food was seaweed. ☐

Vicky yelled angrily down the phone. ☐

2 marks

3) Complete the table below, adding **-ly** to the adjectives to make adverbs.

Adjective	Adverb
kind	kindly
joyful	....
eager	....
sneaky	....

You will have to change the spelling of this adjective when you turn it into an adverb.

2 marks

4) Add your own adverbs to the spaces in this sentence.

George .... swung his bat and hit the ball ....

2 marks

Adverbs

5) Underline the adverb in each sentence below.

The musician strummed his guitar and sang loudly into the microphone.

I gently picked up the friendly green frog and put it in the pond.

The metal box was heavy, but Tom lifted it easily.

Magda opened the door and peered curiously into the kitchen.

Rain was pouring from the sky and the wind was blowing violently.

_____
2 marks

6) Circle the adverb that fits each sentence best.

We might go to the zoo or (**definitely** / **perhaps**) we'll go shopping.

Stealing money from a bank is (**possibly** / **definitely**) illegal.

I'm not sure where Barry is; (**maybe** / **certainly**) he's hiding under there.

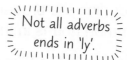
Adverbs can show when or where something is happening, or how likely something is.

_____
2 marks

7) Fill in the blanks with adverbs from the box below.

| soon | everywhere | never | there |

Not all adverbs ends in 'ly'.

Tom rang to say he was coming over ....

Fran was sad to leave London after living .... for six years.

When I dropped the bowl, the cake mix went ....

I like the idea of skydiving, but I have .... tried it.

_____
2 marks

Grammagators sing beautifully about their favourite adverbs. Do you? Tick a box to show how you got on.

Section 1 — Types of Word

Mixed practice

Well done on getting to the end of Section One. There was a lot of grammar in this section, so let's see how much of it you know...

1) In the boxes below, write whether each word is a noun (N), verb (V) or adjective (A).

deliver ☐	**trousers** ☐	**slimy** ☐	**stylish** ☐
receive ☐	**sparkly** ☐	**cliff** ☐	**octopus** ☐

Prove your grammatical knowledge with these exercises — good luck Grammagator.

2) Write the pronoun and the determiner in each sentence in the table below.

Sentence	Pronoun	Determiner
He hated the greedy king.	He	the
We broke a tiny window.		
The queen asked for us.		

2 marks

3) Underline the proper nouns and circle the common nouns in the sentences below.

You can find definitions of the different noun types on page 4.

Kevin gave the bike to Lottie as a present.

In September, the circus will perform in Cambridge.

Millie will take a book to read on the flight to America.

2 marks

4) A word has been underlined in each of the sentences below. Tick the sentence where the underlined word is an abstract noun.

The <u>colony</u> of ants climbed over the mound. ☐

The tall wizard impressed us all with his <u>wisdom</u>. ☐

1 mark

Mixed practice

5) Complete each sentence by forming an adverb from the adjective in brackets.

Kamil ...._calmly_............ (**calm**) took the penalty kick.

The librarian stacked the books .... (**careful**).

My brothers are playing .... (**noisy**) outside.

Anthony .... (**brave**) defended the town from the monster.

_____
2 marks

6) Write the appropriate possessive pronoun to complete each of these sentences.

You paid for the ball, so it is ...._yours_.......... .

We watered our plants while Carl and Nicola watered ....

I ate my apple, but Grace saved .... for later.

_____
2 marks

7) Tick the version of each sentence that is **most** likely to happen.

It might rain tomorrow.	☐	It will rain tomorrow.	☐
You must catch the first train.	☐	You could catch the first train.	☐
I shall be there shortly.	☐	I may be there shortly.	☐

_____
2 marks

8) For each pair of words in brackets, circle the correct form of the noun.

Maha wanted to buy more (**sticker / stickers**) for her collection.

The whole (**class / classes**) was rewarded for good behaviour.

The nurses helped both (**man / men**) get better.

The (**lollys / lollies**) were hidden somewhere else.

_____
2 marks

Mixed practice

9) For each sentence, write in the best adverb
from the options. Use each adverb once.

They were stuck in traffic; .... they were late.   (**there**)

Zack is sitting by himself over ....   (**perhaps**)

.... you should have invited your sister too.   (**now**)

I won't arrive on time if I don't leave ....   (**therefore**)

_____
2 marks

10) Underline the adjective in each sentence.
Then choose another suitable adjective to replace it.

The <u>clever</u> dog made it through the maze.   ...... *speedy* ......

I think chess is a hard game to play.   ....

Hetty liked driving my yellow truck.   ....

He had to throw the burnt pasta in the bin.   ....

_____
2 marks

11) Rewrite each sentence, changing the verbs so that
they are written from a different point of view.

I go to archery practice on a Tuesday.

He goes to archery practice on a Tuesday. ....

My brother builds a tower and then knocks it down.

They ....

We walk to the park and have a picnic.

Zoe ....

_____
2 marks

Mixed practice

12) Read the sentence. Write each word in bold next to the type of word it is.

> **The** weather was **stormy** and it **ruined** our holiday in **Spain**.

Adjective — ....

Verb — ....

Determiner — ....

Proper noun — ....

_____
2 marks

13) Rewrite the sentences below, adding an **adverb** and an **adjective** to each one.

The ballerina danced to the music.

The remarkable ballerina danced perfectly to the music.
....

The tree swayed in the wind.

....

My hamster rolled around in her ball.

....
_____
2 marks

14) Rewrite the passage below, correcting the errors in bold.

My auntie **take** me to the beach when it's sunny. We build **an** sandcastle and **her** buys me an **ice-creams**. I always eat it **quick** so that it doesn't **melts**.

....

....

....

....
_____
2 marks

That was a lot of work, even for a top Grammagator.
How do you feel about Section One now that it's done?

Section 1 — Types of Word

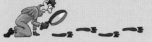

Sentences

Warm Up

Statements, questions, commands and exclamations are all types of sentence.

1) Tick the sentence that is a statement.

When does the show start ☐

Howard boiled the eggs ☐

Close your eyes and count to ten ☐

Now have a go at these questions on sentences.

2) Circle the word in each sentence which shows that it is a command.

Pack some sun cream and a baseball cap.

Before you leave, feed the hamster.

_____
2 marks

3) Complete the table below with a question that matches each statement.

Statement	Question
She doesn't like carrots.	....
The biscuits are over there.	....

_____
2 marks

4) Rewrite the statement below as an exclamation.

The countryside is beautiful.

Exclamations always start with 'what' or 'how', and they must have a verb.

How ....

_____
1 mark

Grammagators know their way around sentences.
Tick a box to show how well you've done.

Paragraphs

Warm Up

Paragraphs break up a text into smaller chunks. Have a go at this warm up question to see if you know when you should use paragraphs...

1) Circle 'true' or 'false' next to each statement.

   You should start a new paragraph when...

   ...a new person speaks.   true / false

   ...you've written too many sentences.   true / false

   ...there is a change in time.   true / false

See if you can answer some more questions on paragraphs.

2) Read this piece of text and mark with a *II* where new paragraphs should begin. You will need to add **three** paragraph markers.

   The rain hammered loudly against the window. Nathan looked out into the garden and sighed. "Cheer up, Nathan," said his brother. "We can go to the zoo tomorrow." Nathan nodded and slumped down in front of the TV. Upstairs, Nathan's sister was busy building a zoo with her stuffed animals. Using pencils as fences, she carefully arranged all the animals around her bedroom. Once she was finished, she went downstairs to get Nathan. She hoped that her pretend zoo would take his mind off the terrible weather.

   _____
   2 marks

3) Write down the reason why the text below needs to be split into two paragraphs.

   Cerys and Saul were on their way to the seaside. The train chugged along slowly as it filled with more and more passengers bound for the beach. After a couple of hours, the conductor announced that they would shortly be arriving at their destination.

   ....
   _____
   1 mark

Paragraphs are no match for a Grammagator.
How well did you tackle them? Tick a box.

Section 2 — Clauses, Phrases and Sentences

Phrases

A phrase is a part of a sentence that does not have a verb or does not have a subject — sometimes it has neither. See if you can spot the phrases in this warm up question.

1) Circle the groups of words that are phrases.

Mobeen has a cold	on the fluffy rug	very carefully
the spiky cactus	we bought a pumpkin	I spilled some squash
he smiled at you	behind the door	they ran away

Practice makes perfect — especially when it comes to phrases. So try these questions out...

2) Tick the sentences where the noun phrase is underlined.

<u>I went</u> to the supermarket near the station. ☐

<u>Mike gave us</u> a slice of cheesecake. ☐

<u>The film about dragons</u> was exciting. ☐

Bakary loves <u>his birthday present</u>. ☐

A noun phrase is a group of words that includes a noun. In a sentence, noun phrases behave like nouns.

2 marks

3) Underline the prepositional phrase in each of these sentences.

I saw a deer running <u>through the forest</u>.

You can leave your umbrella by the front door.

In the garden, they grow tomatoes and lettuce.

The helicopter hovered over the sea.

A preposition tells you where or when something is in relation to other things.

2 marks

Phrases

4) a. Circle the adverbial phrases in the box.

>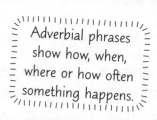
> Adverbial phrases show how, when, where or how often something happens.

too clumsily	last month	very shyly
a short bald man		the snowy mountain

2 marks

b. Use the adverbial phrases you've circled to complete these sentences.

.... , we adopted a cat from a shelter.

Warren dropped the vase because he carried it ....

The children spoke to their teacher ....

2 marks

5) For each of the sentences below, write whether the words in bold are a noun phrase or an adverbial phrase.

The kitten meowed **extremely quietly**. .... adverbial phrase ....

I ate the cookies **as fast as possible**. ....

An usual package arrived at the house. ....

Granny knitted **a multi-coloured scarf**. ....

2 marks

6) Complete each sentence with the type of phrase in the grey box.

.... The short, mysterious witch .... stirred the potion.   noun phrase

The cauldron was ....   prepositional phrase

She added .... to the potion.   noun phrase

2 marks

Section 2 — Clauses, Phrases and Sentences

Clauses

A clause is a part of a sentence that contains both a subject and a verb. Some clauses make sense on their own, but some don't (they might need to be joined to another clause).

1) Tick the groups of words that are clauses.

Amy threw the bottle ☐

under the coffee table ☐

they left the party ☐

quite loudly ☐

Work through these questions to get to grips with more clauses.

2) Circle the clauses that make sense on their own.

| After the sun had set | It was getting late |

| I walked into town | While she was asleep |

| When he'd finished | Nobody heard the phone |

Main clauses make sense on their own, but subordinate clauses don't — they have to be joined to a main clause.

_____
2 marks

3) Write 'M' (for main clause) or 'S' (for subordinate clause) under each of the clauses in the sentences below.

<u>Becky painted a picture</u> <u>while Chen was cooking dinner</u>.

<u>After I'd groomed the horse</u>, <u>I took it to the field</u>.

_____
2 marks

Section 2 — Clauses, Phrases and Sentences   *© CGP — not to be photocopied*

Clauses

4) Put a tick in the correct column to show whether each group of words is a phrase or a clause.

	Phrase	**Clause**
Nancy washed the car		
a large, blue spade		
although Sidra was busy		
next to the calendar		

2 marks

5) Write out the subordinate clause in each sentence below.

The children gasped when they saw the dragon.

when they saw the dragon

Before we left the house, we turned off all the lights.

....

The puppy barked whenever it saw a bird.

....

2 marks

6) Complete each sentence with your own main clause.

a) When they went to the park, *they played hide-and-seek* .

b) .... because it's raining.

c) Even though she was tired, ...

2 marks

Grammagators never pause before a clause. Do you?
Tick a box to show how confident you are with clauses.

© CGP — not to be photocopied

Relative clauses

Warm Up

Relative clauses are a type of subordinate clause. They usually start with a relative pronoun.
Relative clauses give you more information about a noun.

1) Tick the sentences where the relative clause is underlined.

Jerome is the man <u>who owns the llama</u>. ☐

<u>We did everything</u> that we wanted to do. ☐

<u>These are the apples</u> which I bought yesterday. ☐

This is the boy <u>whose mother is an architect</u>. ☐

> Relative pronouns
> are words like 'who',
> 'whom', 'whose',
> 'that' and 'which'.

Test your knowledge of relative clauses with these practice questions.

2) Circle the correct relative pronoun to complete each sentence.

I met the police officer (**that** / **who**) caught the criminal.

Hakim bought a car (**who** / **which**) is bright green.

This is the bookshelf (**that** / **whom**) I built myself.

They had no idea (**whose** / **who**) parrot they'd found.

> You should use 'who',
> 'whom' or 'whose' when
> you're referring to people.

_____
2 marks

3) Join each sentence to its missing relative clause.

| The shark, ... , looked angry. | | which was highly valuable |

| The family, ... , greeted us. | | who had recently moved in |

| The vase, ... , had vanished. | | whose teeth were sharp |

_____
2 marks

Relative clauses

4) Relative pronouns can sometimes be left out of sentences.
Tick the sentences that will still make sense without the relative pronoun in bold.

The secret door **which** we found is over there. ☐

Marzia, **who** has a guide dog, works at my school. ☐

These are the gloves **that** Gareth gave me. ☐

Are you the girl **whose** scarf I borrowed? ☐

2 marks

5) Underline the relative clause in each sentence.
Some of the sentences are written without a relative pronoun.

The party, <u>which my sister organised</u>, was a huge success.

I hid the sweets I collected on Halloween.

The lady, who was tall and elegant, sang sweetly.

We watched the programme you told us about.

2 marks

6) Add your own relative clause to each of the sentences
below, using the relative pronouns from the box.

| whose | that | which |

Use each relative pronoun only once.

The shoes .... are very uncomfortable.

The man .... lives next door.

This is the shop ....

2 marks

Grammagators are relative clause experts. Are you?
Tick a box to show how well you've done.

Section 2 — Clauses, Phrases and Sentences

Mixed practice

Now it's time to practise everything you've learnt in this section.
Ease yourself in with this warm up question...

1) Join each sentence to the correct type.

How busy it is today	question
I entered a talent show	command
Peel all the potatoes	exclamation
What are you doing here	statement

This is where the real mixing begins. See how many of these questions you can answer.

2) Circle 'true' or 'false' next to each statement.

A sentence can contain more than one clause.   **true / false**

Main clauses don't make sense on their own.   **true / false**

Subordinate clauses don't contain a verb.   **true / false**   _____

2 marks

3) Tick the correct column to show whether each
   clause is a main clause or a relative clause.

Clause	Main clause	Relative clause
who we found		
the bird pecked the tree		
everyone chose a colour		
which made a loud noise		

2 marks

Mixed practice

4) Write each of these questions as a command.

Can you wrap the presents?

.....Wrap the presents...

Will you bring a jumper?

....

Are you coming to the concert?

....

_____
2 marks

5) Circle the statements and underline the exclamations.

I can't find the keys   How cold the water is

They won't speak to you   What a friendly horse this is

What a nice meal that was   This is a disaster

_____
2 marks

6) Write 'C' (for clause) or 'P' (for phrase) next to each sentence to show what has been underlined.

Jake tucked his homework <u>inside a textbook</u>. ☐ P

<u>Someone had untied the knot</u> while we weren't looking. ☐

I took off <u>my dirty football socks</u>. ☐

<u>The creature vanished</u> after eating all our snacks. ☐

_____
2 marks

Section 2 — Clauses, Phrases and Sentences

Mixed practice

7) Tick the sentences that contain a relative clause,
   and underline the relative clauses.

   She decided to wait until everyone had gone. ☐

   The hinges, which creak very loudly, need to be oiled. ☐

   This is the cafe where the waitress spilled soup all over me. ☐

   Come to the station with me before you go to the bookshop. ☐

   The lamp that was next to the bed didn't work. ☐

   _____
   2 marks

8) Underline the subordinate clause in each sentence.

   Hannah opened the box <u>even though she'd been told not to</u>.

   When he announced the results, the crowd cheered.

   After he arrived home, Lance went straight to bed.

   The baby giggled happily as it splashed in the water.

   _____
   2 marks

9) Rewrite each sentence with the correct relative pronoun.

   The barn, who has a leaky roof, needs to be repaired.

   ....

   The children that I met yesterday live near the hospital.

   ....

   The toy whose Ichiro broke had to be thrown away.

   ....

   _____
   2 marks

Mixed practice

10) Read this piece of text and mark with a // where new paragraphs should begin. You will need to add **two** paragraph markers.

Today was the big day. Krishna had worked for months on the sculpture, and now it was finally time to unveil it. Six months ago, Krishna would never have believed that she'd be asked to create a sculpture for the town. The phone call from the mayor, the newspaper interviews — it had all felt like a dream. "Ladies and gentlemen," boomed the mayor, "may I welcome you to this unveiling ceremony for our new town sculpture. I'm sure you're all as excited as I am to see what Krishna has created for us."

_____
2 marks

11) Join up each phrase with the correct type.

| the grumpy blue badger | three days ago | extremely harshly | a very smelly piece of cheese |

| adverbial phrase | | noun phrase |

| four chocolate biscuits | despite the weather | your teacher's old hat | surprisingly gently |

_____
2 marks

12) Complete each sentence with your own prepositional phrase.

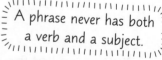
A phrase never has both a verb and a subject.

Larry could see something glittering .... at the bottom of the well ....

We hid ....

I keep my clothes ....

_____
2 marks

Grammagators enjoy a mix of clauses, phrases and sentences as part of a balanced diet. How did you do?

Section 2 — Clauses, Phrases and Sentences

Co-ordinating conjunctions

Warm Up

*Co-ordinating conjunctions are words that join two main clauses,
or that join phrases or words that are equally important...*

1) Tick **one** box to show the sentence that uses a co-ordinating conjunction.

   The tube contained tennis balls. ☐

   Neil ordered pizza and garlic bread. ☐

   > The words 'for', 'and', 'nor', 'but', 'or', 'yet' and 'so' are all co-ordinating conjunctions.

A new section begins — dive right in with some questions on co-ordinating conjunctions.

2) Circle the co-ordinating conjunction in brackets that completes each sentence.

   She can play the drums (**but** / **or**) she can't sing well.

   Molly doesn't enjoy television (**and** / **yet**) she loves films.

   My rabbit wasn't hungry (**but** / **so**) he didn't eat all his carrots.

   ___

   2 marks

3) Join each pair of sentences using **or**, **and** or **but**.

   Luke wants to go to the park. He has a cold.

   Luke wants to go to the park **but** he has a cold.
   ....

   Anila likes painting. She likes writing.

   ....

   You can sit at the front. You can sit at the back.

   ....

   We went to buy a horse. The shop was closed.

   ....

   ___

   2 marks

*Co-ordinating conjunctions sound tough, but they're
no match for a Grammagator. How did you find them?*

Subordinating conjunctions

Subordinating conjunctions join main clauses to subordinate clauses.

1)   Circle all the subordinating conjunctions in the box below.

> when   and
>
> (if)   nor   unless
>
> for   yet   because

It's time to use conjunctions to link up some main clauses and subordinate clauses.

2)   Tick the sentences that use subordinating conjunctions correctly.

I haven't seen Hayley since she moved away. ☐

He won't get dessert whether he finishes his dinner. ☐

Before it gets too late, we should build a camp fire. ☐

I love mangoes rather than Satoshi prefers melons. ☐

2 marks

3)   Draw lines to match each sentence with the correct missing subordinating conjunction.

Lucy will win .... she scores now.		although
.... it's tiring, Max likes doing cartwheels.		when
We surprised Pete .... he got home.		if
I'll draw a clown .... I saw one yesterday.		because

2 marks

Grammagators can use subordinating conjunctions to link their clauses. Do you think you can do it too?

Prepositions

Warm Up

Prepositions tell you how things are related in a sentence. For example, they can tell you when, where or why something happens. Try to spot some prepositions...

1) Tick the words and phrases that can be used as prepositions.

| before ☐ | put ☐ | because of ☐ | twice ☐ |
| valley ☐ | in ☐ | butterfly ☐ | during ☐ |

Let's get stuck into some more preposition exercises.

2) Underline the preposition in each sentence.

He placed the delicious cookies on the desk.

Miranda received an award after the match.

My dog stole the sausages and leapt over my neighbour's fence.

_____
2 marks

3) Circle the preposition in brackets that completes each sentence.

Jim kept laughing (**during** / **behind**) the sad parts of the play.

I hid my brother's favourite toy (**beside** / **until**) the fridge.

I hope my parrot will learn to talk (**in** / **by**) the end of the year.

_____
2 marks

4) Fill in the blanks with prepositions from the box below.

into   around   until

Tariq nervously paced .... the room.

I don't have to help paint the garage .... tomorrow.

The rat scurried off .... the night.

_____
2 marks

Prepositions

5) Tick the **two** sentences where the preposition shows place.
Circle the preposition in each sentence you've ticked.

I keep my lucky necklace under my bed. ☐

Stuart told lots of jokes throughout the show. ☐

The balloon floated above her head. ☐

2 marks

6) Draw a line from each sentence to show whether the prepositions
in bold tell you when or where something happens.

| The spaceship rocketed **into** the sky. |
| The parcel will be here **within** two hours. |
| There was a shark **beneath** the water. |
| We went home **after** the parade. |

when

where

2 marks

7) Complete this sentence by adding a preposition that shows cause.
Remember that a preposition can be made up of more than one word.

Natalie was late .... the traffic.

1 mark

8) Rewrite the sentence below with different prepositions to replace the words
in bold. Don't worry if the meaning of the sentence changes.

Walk **along** the river and go **through** the waterfall **after** the shipwreck.

....

....

2 marks

*Grammagators are as chilled as ice cubes about
prepositions. Do you feel as cool about them?*

Section 3 — Conjunctions and Prepositions

Mixed practice

You're nearing the end of another section, so it's time to see what you've learnt...

1) Circle all of the co-ordinating conjunctions below.

although	and	without	nor

so	while	but	indeed

Just a few more exercises on conjunctions and prepositions to go.

2) Join each word or phrase (in a white box) with the type of word it is (in a grey box).

or	under	though	onto	unless

co-ordinating conjunction	subordinating conjunction	preposition

_____
2 marks

3) Circle the subordinating conjunction in brackets that completes each sentence.

The goat escaped (**while** / **so that**) the farmer was away.

(**Once** / **Until**) Kim finishes her chores, she will go swimming with Chris.

Juan fixed the pool table (**when** / **rather than**) getting rid of it.

_____
2 marks

4) Tick the sentences that use prepositions.

Cook the spinach after the carrots. ☐

Although the cake looked nice, it tasted awful. ☐

I trekked across the vast desert. ☐

The ground was very uneven so I fell over. ☐

_____
2 marks

Mixed practice

5) Underline the conjunction in each sentence.

Carol hates camels but she likes llamas.

We all woke up early because we were going on holiday.

The hedgehogs hibernate in the shed and the dormice sleep in the hedge.

Keith might want the lobster or he might want the crab instead.

_____
2 marks

6) Add a conjunction to complete each sentence.

I saw thousands of sheep .... I went to Cumbria.

.... my legs hurt, I want to climb this mountain.

Tanvi gave me some yoghurt .... she didn't have any herself.

_____
2 marks

7) For each sentence below, write whether the preposition
in bold shows time, place or cause.

I'm not seeing the tigers **until** midday. ....

We often go for drives **along** the coast. ....

The match was cancelled **because of** the storm. ....

The meerkat leapt **into** the hole. ....

We got to the park **before** everyone else. ....

_____
2 marks

Subject and object

Warm Up

Most sentences have a subject and an object. The subject is a person or thing doing or being something, and the object has something done to it.

1)   Circle the subject in each sentence.

      Pasha carefully ironed his shirt.

      The magician pulled a rabbit from his hat.

      In two weeks, I am going on holiday.

Practise your subject and object skills by answering these questions.

2)   Tick the box underneath the object in each sentence.

     a. <u>Mum</u> made <u>lasagne</u> for tea.

     b. <u>Yusef</u> brushed <u>his teeth</u>.

     c. <u>I</u> closed <u>the blinds</u> in my room.

 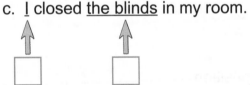

     d. <u>The fireworks</u> lit up <u>the night sky</u>.

_____
2 marks

3)   For each of the sentences below, write whether the words in bold are the subject or the object.

     The parrot repeated everything I said.   .... subject ....

     Penny is learning to play **the piano**.   ....

     After lunch, **we** are going to the cinema.   ....

     The teacher folded **the piece of paper**.   ....

_____
2 marks

Grammagators know their subjects from their objects. How well did you tackle them? Tick a box.

Active and passive voice

Warm Up

In an active sentence, the subject does something. In a passive sentence, something is done to the subject. Have a go at this warm up question...

1) Tick the sentence that is written in the active voice.

   The plumber unblocked the drain. ☐

   The bench was painted by Diana. ☐

Test your active and passive voice skills with some more practice questions.

2) Write 'P' in the boxes next to the passive sentences.

   The shoe was buried by the dog. ☐

   The lights flickered during the storm. ☐

   I thought the film was boring. ☐

   Carmen was surprised by the news. ☐

   In passive sentences, the word 'by' can introduce who does the action.

   2 marks

3) a. Rearrange the words to make a sentence in the active voice.
   Make sure you punctuate the sentence correctly.

   | the | stole | thief | rubies | the |

   ....

   1 mark

   b. Rewrite the sentence in the passive voice.
   You will need to include extra words.

   ....

   1 mark

An active Grammagator has no problem spotting a passive. How active are you? Tick a box.

Section 4 — Sentence Structure and Tense

Past, present and future tenses

The past tense shows you that something has finished. The present tense shows you what's happening now or what happens regularly. The future tense shows you what will happen.

1) Circle the boxes where the verb is in the present tense.

| we hopped | you jump | I try | they laugh |

| she picks | they will go | he gripped | you imagine |

Here's some more tenses practice.

2) Write whether each sentence is about the past, the present or the future.

You will meet my grandma next week.   .... future ....

After school, we rehearsed the play.   ....

I'm waiting for my dessert.   ....

I will call you when I get home.   ....

2 marks

3) a. Tick the sentence that uses tenses incorrectly.

I overslept so I miss the bus to school.   ☐

We visited the museum before we left.   ☐

They know the answer, but they refuse to tell me.   ☐

1 mark

b. Rewrite the sentence you ticked so that it uses tenses correctly.

....

1 mark

Past, present and future tenses

4)   Circle the verb in brackets that correctly completes each sentence.

Last year, I (**went** / **will go**) on a school trip to London.

Tomorrow, you (**will need** / **needed**) to leave early.

She (**wanted** / **wants**) to be a chef when she is older.

2 marks

5)   Complete each sentence with the correct verbs from the box.

needed	ran	was	~~flipped~~	ate	fell

Use each verb only once.

Greg   _flipped_   the pancake and it _____ on the floor.

We _____ out of cereal, so we _____ toast instead.

I _____ to go to the shop, but it _____ closed.

2 marks

6)   Rewrite the sentences below, changing them into the tense in brackets.

I make cookies with my sister. We sell them at the bake sale.   (**past**)

....

....

Mei played netball at school. She was the best player.   (**present**)

....

....

2 marks

Grammagators love talking about the past, the present and the future. How confident do you feel? Tick a box.

Section 4 — Sentence Structure and Tense

Past tense with 'have'

Warm Up

The past tense with 'have' is used to talk about something that has happened recently, e.g. I have been to the dentist.

1) Underline the present perfect form in each sentence.

   They <u>have eaten</u> their lunch.

   Jordanna has beaten my score.

   I have fixed the broken shelf.

   Martyn and Emir have apologised.

> The past tense with 'have' is sometimes called the 'present perfect form'.

Now you've done the warm up, get stuck into these questions.

2) Complete the sentences below by adding 'have' or 'has'.

   The bear .... been asleep all winter.

   I hope you .... locked the back door.

   He .... given some money to charity.

   Ailsa and I .... known each other for years.

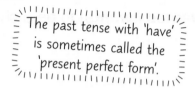

———
2 marks

3) Rewrite the sentences below using the present perfect form.

   The boat set sail.

   ....

   The farmer milked the cows.

   ....

———
2 marks

Grammagators are always on perfect form with the past tense. Are you? Tick a box to show how you did.

Verbs with '-ing'

Warm Up

Verbs with 'ing' can be used to show that something is happening right now or was happening at a certain time in the past. Try this warm up question...

1) Circle the correct word in brackets to form the present progressive.

You (**am** / **are** / **is**) sweeping the floor.

He (**am** / **are** / **is**) drinking some orange juice.

I (**am** / **are** / **is**) turning the computer off.

> The present tense with '-ing' is also called the 'present progressive'.

Let's keep going with some more questions on verbs with '-ing'.

2) Write the verbs in bold in the present progressive form.

Kyle **teaches** English in Spain. ....is teaching.................

The police **investigate** the burglary. ....

I **sit** in the lounge with Kwame. ....

My nephew **catches** insects in the garden. ....

2 marks

3) Complete the table using the correct form of 'to be' and the '-ing' form of each verb.

> The past tense with '-ing' is also called the 'past progressive'.

Verb	Past tense with '-ing'
to fly	The pilot ....was flying........ the plane.
to argue	They .... about the game.
to skip	The children .... to school.
to brush	Latoya .... her hair.

2 marks

When it comes to this topic, Grammagators put the '-ing' in 'amazing'. How did you do? Tick a box.

Section 4 — Sentence Structure and Tense

Mixed practice

There's been a lot of tense talk in this section, so it's time to round it off with some mixed practice. Start by answering this warm up question...

1) Circle the verb in brackets that correctly completes each sentence.

Last weekend, I (**finished** / **finish**) my book.

He (**runs** / **ran**) to school when he's late.

We (**leave** / **left**) early because I was tired.

Shona (**won** / **wins**) the class quiz yesterday.

Now test your sentence structure and tense skills with these questions.

2) Tick the correct box to show whether each sentence is in the present progressive or the past progressive.

	present progressive	past progressive
I was riding my horse in the field.	☐	☐
We are making a present for Dad.	☐	☐
They are following the path carefully.	☐	☐

2 marks

3) One verb in each of these sentences is incorrect.
Underline the incorrect verb and write the correct form on the line.

I was making a drink when you <u>phone</u>. ....*phoned*.............

He is writes a letter and will send it tomorrow. ....

Do you cleaned your teeth regularly? ....

Yesterday, we collect our puppy and brought it home. ....

I want to buy a tree so I can planted it in my garden. ....

2 marks

Mixed practice

4) Complete each sentence with the present perfect form of the verb in brackets.

We .... (**open**) all our presents.

No one .... (**watch**) the cartoon before.

Who .... (**ask**) to see me?

Harriet .... (**take**) the last jam tart.

> Remember, the 'present perfect form' is the past tense with 'have'.

———
2 marks

5) a. Tick the sentence that is written in the passive voice.

Walter left his shoes by the radiator. ☐

The seal was grabbed by the shark. ☐

The ship sailed past the jagged rocks. ☐

———
1 mark

b. Rewrite the sentence that you ticked in the active voice.

....
———
1 mark

6) Write two sentences using the subject and object given in the boxes.

Subject: giraffe   Object: leaves

....

Subject: dog   Object: stick

....
———
2 marks

Section 4 — Sentence Structure and Tense

Section 5 — Writing Style

Standard vs. Non-Standard

Standard English follows the normal spelling, punctuation and grammar rules.
Non-Standard English is a more informal type of English.

1) Tick the sentence that is written in Standard English.

We bought those tickets online. ☐

Esma always walks too slow. ☐

Mrs Potts didn't see nothing suspicious. ☐

Here are some more practice questions on Standard vs. Non-Standard English.

2) Join each sentence to the missing word that completes it in Standard English.

I followed ... into the woods.

We won't need all of ... ingredients.

Did Cyrus build ... snowmen?

You will meet ... at the station.

them

those

2 marks

3) Complete each sentence with the correct word from the box.

seen	was	gone	saw	went	were

Davit and Timur .... to the supermarket.

We .... stranded on a desert island.

I thought I .... something in the trees.

Before her audition, she .... very nervous.

You won't need to use all of the words.

2 marks

Standard vs. Non-Standard

4) Circle the word that completes each sentence in Standard English.

She asked (**me** / I) and Selina to carry the bags.

(**Me** / I) thought I'd left my jacket at home.

At midnight, my brother and (**me** / I) crept downstairs.

_____
2 marks

5) Tick the box under the word in each sentence that shows it is in Non-Standard English. Write a correction for each word on the lines.

If we walk quick, we might still get there on time.   ....

I'm not good at P.E., but I'm doing really good in art.   ....

_____
2 marks

6) Rewrite the sentences below in Standard English.

You'll need to change two words in each sentence.

You was wrong about them boys.

...... You were wrong about those boys. ....

I should of done the work what you gave me.

....

Kenzo ain't got no brothers.

....

_____
2 marks

Grammagators have high standards when it comes to written English. Tick a box to show how you've done.

© *CGP — not to be photocopied*   *Section 5 — Writing Style*

Formal and informal writing

Warm Up

Formal writing is used when you're writing something important or when you're writing to someone you don't know. Informal writing is much chattier and friendlier.

1) For each pair of sentences, write 'F' next to the formal version and 'I' next to the informal version.

We were scared stiff! ☐   **We were very afraid.** ☐

I discarded my litter. ☐   **I binned my litter.** ☐

Let's see how well you can tackle some more questions.

2) Draw lines to join each informal sentence with the matching formal sentence.

I haven't seen him.   Iona was incredibly happy.

You're coming, aren't you?   Are you coming?

He's winding me up.   I have not seen him.

Grab your stuff now.   He is irritating me.

Iona was really chuffed.   Collect your belongings now.

2 marks

3) Use **one** of the words from the box to complete the sentence in the subjunctive form.

The subjunctive is used in very formal writing. Examples of the subjunctive include "If I were you..." and "It is vital that he dance at the wedding..."

| visiting | visit | visited |

It is important that she .... the tiger enclosure today.

1 mark

Writing is always a formal affair for a Grammagator. Do you know how to use formal writing? Tick a box.

Mixed practice

It's time to put what you've learnt about writing styles to the test.

1) Circle the word that completes each sentence in Standard English.

You (**took** / **taken**) a photo of the view.

I (**came** / **come**) home early last night.

They (**did** / **done**) all the work themselves.

Now give these mixed practice questions a go.

2) Write 'S' (for Standard English) or 'N' (for Non-Standard English) next to each of the sentences below.

Kadir went to the dentist after school. $\boxed{\text{S}}$

I would have cleaned the windows for you. $\square$

We ain't got nothing to do with it. $\square$

She liked the cake what I made for her. $\square$

2 marks

3) Write whether each sentence is an example of formal or informal writing.

Tyrone was an elderly gentleman. .... formal ....

The kids were messing about outside. ....

Greta'd like to know what's going on. ....

Unfortunately, my answer was incorrect. ....

They dared you to do it, didn't they? ....

2 marks

Mixed practice

4) Join each sentence to the word that completes it in Standard English.

ain't		There isn't ... left in the fridge.		I
nothing		This ... what I was looking for.		isn't
anything		Tonya and ... waved to him.		me

2 marks

5) For each sentence, circle the more formal word in brackets.

Can you (**help** / **assist**) me with my homework?

They didn't have time to (**scoff** / **eat**) their breakfast.

Damla (**dumped** / **put**) her coat on the table.

Everyone was (**very** / **mega**) excited about the trip.

He (**hit** / **bashed**) his head when he fell over.

2 marks

6) Each sentence below contains one word that isn't in Standard English.
Underline the incorrect words and rewrite them correctly on the lines.

The farmer saw some cows what had escaped. ....

The cows mooed loud and ran away. ....

"Them pesky cows!" said the farmer. ....

He were angry because he had to catch the cows. ....

2 marks

Grammagators never get their tails in a twist when tackling writing style questions. Do you? Tick a box.

Word families

Warm Up

Word families are groups of words that contain the same root.
Their meanings are related — like a family.

1) All the words below belong to the same word family.
   Write the root word on the line.

   | crossroads | | crossword | | across | | crossing |

   ....

You're not done with word families yet — try these questions out for size.

2) Complete the table to show which words belong to the same word family.
   The first row has been done for you.

	racetrack	treetop	windsurf	printer
windmill	✗	✗	✓	✗
racer				
footprint				
treehouse				

   _____
   2 marks

3) Look at the word family below.
   What does the root '**cent**' mean? Tick **one** box.

   century   **centimetre**   **percentage**

   year ☐   hundred ☐

   maths ☐   measure ☐

   _____
   1 mark

Prefixes

Now have a go at these questions on prefixes.

2) Split the words below into a prefix and a root word.

	prefix	**root word**
uncover ⟹	un	cover
uphill ⟹	....	....
export ⟹	....	....

2 marks

3) Add a prefix from the box below to each word so that it means the opposite.

ir	~~dis~~	un	il	de	im

Use each prefix only once.

..dis.. respect   ....moral   ....regular

...........legal   ....even   ....construct

2 marks

4) Rewrite the sentence below, changing the underlined prefix to create a new noun.

Kendis got a new <u>bi</u>cycle for Christmas.

....

1 mark

Prefixes

5) Make three words using the prefixes in the white box
and the root words in the grey box.

fore	in	photo

graph	head	form

....

6) The prefixes in bold in these sentences are incorrect.
Rewrite the words with the correct prefixes in the space provided.

The scientists used a **super**marine to reach the seabed.

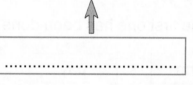

....

Phoebe made some popcorn in the **trans**wave.

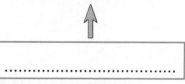

....

The athlete wrote his **anti**graph on a napkin.

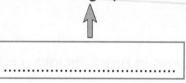

....

2 marks

7) Explain how the different prefixes in the two
sentences below change their meanings.

Robin **reread** the sign.

This means that Robin ....

Robin **misread** the sign.

This means that Robin ....

2 marks

Grammagators like to get words off to a good start.
Do you? Tick a box to show how confident you feel.

Section 6 — Making and Choosing Words

Suffixes

Suffixes are letters that you add to the end of a word to change the word's meaning.

1) Underline the suffix in each word below.

agreement   handful   kindness   spraying

former   majority   priceless

There are lots of different suffixes that you can add to words.
Do these practice questions to help you get the hang of them.

2) Join each word to the correct suffix. The first one has been done for you.

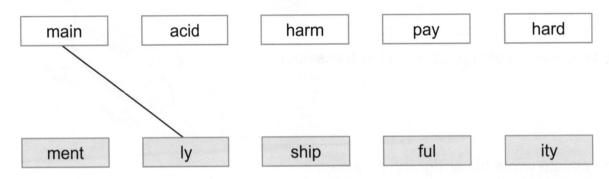

main	acid	harm	pay	hard

ment	ly	ship	ful	ity

2 marks

3) Use the suffixes from the box to turn each word in brackets into a noun.

~~ty~~	ity	ment	er	ness

Use each suffix only once.

The dog was praised for its ......loyalty...... (**loyal**).

The school bought some new sports .... (**equip**).

In .... (**real**), Sophie didn't know what she was doing.

The window .... (**clean**) climbed her ladder carefully.

"Cake is my biggest .... (**weak**)," admitted Nadeem.

2 marks

Section 6 — Making and Choosing Words

Suffixes

4) Circle two suffixes that can be added to each word below to create adjectives.

friend (ly)   ity   ate   (less)

thought   less   ness   ful   ify

disgust   ate   ed   ing   ment

2 marks

5) Circle the word with the correct suffix in each sentence.

Salma (**carelessty** / **carelessly**) slammed the door.

He is a very (**logical** / **logicate**) person.

They were looking for (**talenting** / **talented**) dancers.

I was (**hopeful** / **hopely**) that my cat would be found.

2 marks

6) Rewrite the sentences so that the words in bold have the correct suffixes.

Mum still talks to her **childship** friends.

Mum still talks to her childhood friends.
....

A new **amuseness** park has opened near our town.

....

My Christmas list was **endful** — I wanted lots of presents.

....

2 marks

All Grammagators keep a few suffixes up their sleeves.
Do you? Tick a box to show how well you did.

Section 6 — Making and Choosing Words

Making verbs

Warm Up

You can use suffixes to make words into verbs. Have a go at this warm up question.

1) Complete each verb by drawing a line to the correct suffix.

| Giorgio plan_ | he catch_ | Victoria wish_ | she eat_ |

| s | | es |

Answer these practice questions to test your verb-making skills.

2) Underline the verb with the correct suffix to complete each sentence.

The dog is (**<u>listening</u>** / **listens**) to the music.

At first, I (**believed** / **believes**) what you told me.

Quinn was (**paints** / **painting**) Lily's portrait.

They were lost, so they (**calling** / **called**) for help.

You (**changes** / **changed**) your socks three times yesterday.

_____
2 marks

3) Complete each sentence by adding **-ed** or **-ing** to the word in brackets.

> The spelling of the word in brackets may need to change.

Jin ......**poured**...... (**pour**) cream on his strawberries.

The children were .... (**hope**) to meet the Queen.

Today, we are .... (**celebrate**) Amanda's birthday.

The ghost had .... (**haunt**) the castle for centuries.

His parents .... (**worry**) about him all the time.

_____
2 marks

Section 6 — Making and Choosing Words   *© CGP — not to be photocopied*

Making verbs

4) Tick the sentences where the verb in bold is correct.

I was **watched** TV when the phone rang. ☐

They always **asks** a lot of questions. ☐

You are **behaving** brilliantly today. ☐

She **wants** to go fishing after dinner. ☐

_____
2 marks

5) a. Add the correct suffix from the box to turn each root word into a verb.

| ise | ate | ify | en |

You'll need to use some suffixes more than once.

modern .....ise.....   tight ....   final ....

decor ....   simpl ....   length ....

_____
2 marks

b. Choose one of the verbs from part a and use it in a sentence.

....
1 mark

6) Write a sentence on each of the lines using the verb and the suffix given.

rush + es

....

think + ing

....
_____
2 marks

     Section 6 — Making and Choosing Words

Synonyms

Warm Up

A synonym is a word that has the same, or nearly the same, meaning as another word.

1)   Tick the words that are synonyms of '**complain**'.

support ☐   **praise** ☐   **protest** ☐

moan ☐   **encourage** ☐   **grumble** ☐

Now you've warmed up, have a go at some more practice questions about synonyms.

2)   Join each word on the left to its synonym on the right.

pretend		rude
impolite		change
alter		fake
mend		repair

2 marks

3)   Circle the **two** words in each sentence that are synonyms of each other.

I don't like these sour oranges — their juice is too sharp.

It was a difficult challenge — everyone had found it tough.

2 marks

4)   Write a suitable synonym for each word in bold.

Nerissa reacted **furiously** to the news.   ....

The cat **strolled** across the garden.   ....

2 marks

Grammagators think synonyms are great, fantastic, superb and wonderful. What do you think of them?

Section 6 — Making and Choosing Words

Antonyms

Warm Up

An antonym is a word that means the opposite of another word.

1) Circle the words that are antonyms of '**narrow**'.

wide	broad	small

tight	cramped	thick

It's time for some more practice with antonyms. Give these questions a go.

2) Tick the pairs of words which are antonyms.

close / nearby ☐   timid / afraid ☐

entertaining / boring ☐   stained / clean ☐

lazy / energetic ☐   empty / vacant ☐

2 marks

3) Complete each sentence with an antonym of the underlined word.

Kayode's marbles are <u>colourful</u>, but mine are ....

My neighbour likes to <u>frown</u>, but I prefer to ....

Fredrik wants to <u>sell</u> his hotel and we would like to .... it.

2 marks

4) Write an antonym of the word below on the line next to it.
Then use the antonym you have written in a sentence.

excellent ➡ ....

....

2 marks

*True Grammagators can track down any antonym.
Can you? Tick a box to show how well you did.*

Section 6 — Making and Choosing Words

Mixed practice

Warm Up

You're almost at the end of the book! There are just a few
more practice questions standing in your way...

1) Tick the sentences that use suffixes correctly.

   The fearly knight ran away from the powerness dragon. ☐

   Her apartment is spotless — she cleans it every day. ☐

   The secretive millionaire tried to hide his identity. ☐

   The colourate unicorn galloped cheerfulment towards me. ☐

Keep going — there's still plenty of mixed practice for you to get stuck into.

2) Write whether each pair of words are synonyms or antonyms.

   loving / cruel ....antonyms.............................

   peculiar / ordinary ....

   amusing / funny ....

   neglect / abandon ....

   2 marks

3) The box contains two groups of four words belonging to the same word family.
   Find and complete the groups on each of the dotted lines below.

   | ~~daytime~~ | unseen | lifetime | oversee |
   | ~~foresee~~ | timeless | seeing | timeline |

   daytime ....

   foresee ....

   2 marks

Mixed practice

4) Add the suffix to the root word and write the new word on the line.

trap + ed ⟹ ....

sob + ing ⟹ ....

dry + ed ⟹ ....

wave + ing ⟹ ....

2 marks

5) a. Use the prefixes and root words below to make four different words.

Prefixes		Root words		
semi	~~mis~~	~~placed~~	stand	
under	tele		vision	circle

Only use each prefix and root word once.

...... misplaced ......

2 marks

b. Use the words from part a to complete the sentences below.

Marco watched a documentary on the ....

A .... is half of a circle.

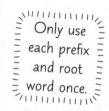

I didn't .... what the woman was saying.

The wizard had .... his magic wand.

2 marks

6) Write a sentence using the verb **tidy** with the suffix **-s**.

....

Write a sentence using the verb **chop** with the suffix **-ed**.

....

2 marks

© CGP — not to be photocopied

Section 6 — Making and Choosing Words

Glossary

Active — Sentences where the subject of the sentence does the action of the verb.

Adjective — A word that describes a noun, e.g. **big** house, **cold** morning.

Adverb — A word that describes a verb, an adjective or other adverbs.

Adverbial — A word, or group of words, that behaves like an adverb. It gives more information about a verb or clause.

Antonyms — Words that mean the opposite, e.g. **big** and **small**.

Clause — Part of a sentence that contains a subject and a verb.

Conjunction — A word that joins two clauses or sentences, e.g. **and**, **but**, **so**.

Determiner — A word that tells you if a noun is general or specific, e.g. **the**, **a** or **an**.

Main clause — A clause that makes sense on its own,

e.g. **I went out even though it was raining.**

This bit is the main clause because 'I went out' makes sense on its own.

Modal verb — A verb that can show how likely something is, e.g. **We might go out.**

Noun — A word that names something, e.g. **Paul**, **scissors**, **herd**, **happiness**.

Object — The part of the sentence that the action of the verb is being done to.

Passive — Sentences where the subject has something done to it.

Glossary

Phrase — A small part of a sentence, usually without a verb.

Possessive pronoun — A pronoun which shows who owns something, e.g. **mine**, **hers**.

Prefix — Letters that can be put in front of a word to change its meaning, e.g. **un**lock.

Preposition — A word that tells you how things are related, e.g. **in**, **above**, **before**.

Pronoun — Words that can be used instead of nouns, e.g. **I**, **you**, **he**, **it**.

Relative clause — A type of subordinate clause that tells you more about a noun. It is often introduced by a relative pronoun, e.g. **She's the girl <u>who</u> likes onions.**

Relative pronoun — A pronoun that introduces a relative clause, e.g. **who**, **which**, **that**.

Subject — The person or thing doing the action of the verb.

Subordinate clause — A clause which doesn't make sense on its own, e.g. **<u>While you were out</u>, I watched TV.**

This bit is the subordinate clause because 'While you were out' doesn't make sense on its own.

Suffix — Letters that can be put after a word to change its meaning, e.g. play**ful**.

Synonyms — Words that mean the same, e.g. **large** and **big**.

Verb — A doing or being word, e.g. I **run**, he **went**, you **are**.

Scoresheet

Fill in your scores below, then add them up to find your total marks.

Section 1	Score
Nouns	/ 4
Singular and plural nouns	/ 4
Types of noun	/ 12
Pronouns	/ 14
Determiners	/ 6
Verbs	/ 22
Adjectives	/ 12
Adverbs	/ 12
Mixed practice	/ 25
Total for Section 1	**/ 111**
Section 2	**Score**
Sentences	/ 5
Paragraphs	/ 3
Phrases	/ 12
Clauses	/ 10
Relative clauses	/ 10
Mixed practice	/ 22
Total for Section 2	**/ 62**
Section 3	**Score**
Co-ordinating conjunctions	/ 4
Subordinating conjunctions	/ 4
Prepositions	/ 13
Mixed practice	/ 12
Total for Section 3	**/ 33**

Section 4	Score
Subject and object	/ 4
Active and passive voice	/ 4
Past, present and future tenses	/ 10
Past tense with 'have'	/ 4
Verbs with '-ing'	/ 4
Mixed practice	/ 10
Total for Section 4	**/ 36**
Section 5	**Score**
Standard vs. Non-Standard	/ 10
Formal and informal writing	/ 3
Mixed practice	/ 10
Total for Section 5	**/ 23**
Section 6	**Score**
Word families	/ 3
Prefixes	/ 11
Suffixes	/ 10
Making verbs	/ 11
Synonyms	/ 6
Antonyms	/ 6
Mixed practice	/ 12
Total for Section 6	**/ 59**
Total for Book	**324**

Look at your total score to see how you're doing and where you need more practice:

0 – 194 — You've made a good start. Revise grammar and then have another go.

195 – 275 — You're doing well. Have another look at any sections you're struggling with.

276 – 324 — You're doing really well. Give yourself a pat on the back.